Hanna-Barbera's

TOP CAT
ANNUAL

CONTENTS

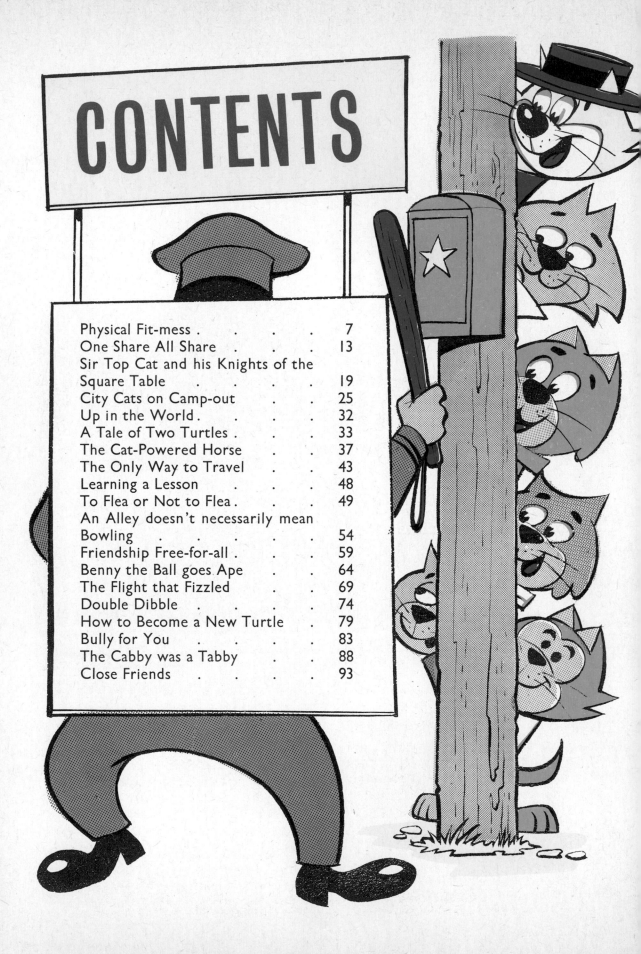

Hanna-Barbera TOP CAT — PHYSICAL FIT-MESS

OF ALL THE LAZY, UNHEALTHY, LOAFING, OUT OF CONDITION BUNCH OF CATS...

JUST A MINUTE, DIBBLE! WHAT KIND OF CONDITION ARE YOU SUGGESTING WE'RE *OUT* OF?

PHYSICAL CONDITION, WHAT ELSE? YOU GUYS DON'T GET ENOUGH EXERCISE!

(YAWN!) JUST GETTING UP IS ENOUGH EXERCISE FOR ME!

MENTAL EXERCISE IS MORE TO MY LIKING!

I'M AFRAID I'D LOSE WEIGHT IF I EXERCISED!

SO WE DON'T EXERCISE, SO WHAT?

SO, IT'S DOWNRIGHT UNPATRIOTIC TO BE AS FLABBY AS YOU FELINES!

UNPATRIOTIC?

SURE! HAVEN'T YOU BEEN READING THE PAPERS? THE COUNTRY'S LEADERS SAY WE SHOULD BECOME MORE PHYSICALLY FIT!

WHY, THE PRESIDENT HIMSELF SUGGESTS WE ALL DO A FEW SIMPLE EXERCISES!

THE *PRESIDENT?*

SIMPLE EXERCISES, EH? WELL, WE'RE JUST AS PATRIOTIC AS THE NEXT GUY!

JUST AS SIMPLE, TOO!

LET'S JUST HAVE A LOOK AT WHAT FOLKS ARE DOING TO KEEP FIT AND WE'LL DO THE SAME!

FIFTY-MILE HIKES! (ULP!) IF THAT'S SIMPLE, I'M A DACHSHUND!

FIFTY-MILE HIKES

I DIDN'T FIGURE YOU SISSIES HAD THE GET-UP AND GO TO MAKE MUSCLES FOR YOURSELVES!

ARE WE GOING TO LET HIM SAY THAT?

NO! WE'RE GOING TO GET UP AND GO...ON A FIFTY-MILE HIKE!

FORWARD FOR THE HONOUR OF THE GROUP!

SHORTLY...

WE'RE HIKING OVER TO ELMWOOD WHICH IS EXACTLY FIFTY MILES AWAY!

I'LL BE AT THE CITY LIMITS TO MEET YOU...IF YOU EVER GET THERE! HA,HA!

15

MEANWHILE... QUICK, HENRY...GET ME THE NEW TAILOR-MADE TIE AND HAT! HERE COMES SPOOK!

GOSH, WITH OFFICER DIBBLE FOLLOWING ME, I'M TOO NERVOUS TO EAT MY POPCORN!

HM, AMAZING! HE'S WORTH A BILLION DOLLARS AND STILL LOOKS JUST THE SAME!

I SUPPOSE HE WANTS TO SHARE AND SHARE ALIKE, TOO!

HERE'S YOUR NEW HAT, MR. SPOOK! AND I'LL JUST GET RID OF THIS OLD TIE FOR YOU!

HUH?

THIS NEW ONE HAS 24-CARAT GOLD WOVEN INTO IT!

GEE, THANKS... MY OLD ONE ONLY HAD EGGS SPLATTERED ON IT!

I FEEL LIKE A BILLIONAIRE!

I'LL JUST ADD IT TO THE ACCOUNT, LIKE TOP CAT SAID!

SO TOP CAT IS RESPONSIBLE FOR ALL THIS! I'LL HAVE TO GO AND APOLOGISE FOR NOT SHARING MY GOOD FORTUNE SOONER!

I'LL TAKE A SHORT CUT THROUGH THE HOTEL RITZ! AT LEAST I'M DRESSED FOR IT!

BOY, SPOOK SURE MAKES MY JOB TOUGH!

17

SIR TOP CAT and his KNIGHTS of the SQUARE TABLE

REMEMBER, GUYS, AS MEMBERS OF THE **BACK ALLEY KNIGHTS OF THE ROUND TABLE,** WE MUST DECORATE OUR CLUBHOUSE ACCORDINGLY!

SAY, THIS IS A SWELL CLUB YOU DREAMED UP, TOP CAT!

FREE DUMP

JUNK YARD

HEY! I FOUND AN OLD DANCING SLIPPER!

NOW, WHAT'S A KNIGHT OF THE ROUND TABLE WANT WITH THAT?

I FORGOT...KNIGHTS ARE ROUGH AND TOUGH!

HERE'S A HORSESHOE! I HAVE A FEELING THAT THIS IS GOING TO BE OUR LUCKY DAY, BOYS!

CLANK!

HEY! WHAT WAS THAT?

GEE! LOOK AT THE SIZE OF THAT **MIRROR!**

LUCKY THAT HORSESHOE DIDN'T BREAK IT!

23

31

UP IN THE WORLD

Snagglepuss was in a gay mood as he hurried to the moving picture studio. He had been called that very morning and told that there was an acting part for him in a new picture that was being filmed.

"It's hard work," the man had warned him.

"It's a job, so I'll take it," Snagglepuss had replied, remembering the words of his grandfather, Snagglepuss the First: "Getting to the top isn't easy, but if you take a job once in awhile, it helps!"

"I'll show granddaddy yet," Snagglepuss thought as he approached the studio.

Entering the sound stage where he was to act out his scene, Snagglepuss reported at once to the director.

"This is what you have to do," the director told him. "You're playing the part of a mountaineer. You're tired, thirsty, and hungry. But you are determined to climb to the summit," he explained. "Do you understand?" he asked in conclusion.

"Perfectly, sir," Snagglepuss assured him. "You'll see the finest performance I can give. My heart will be in it!"

So, with a pack on his back, a pick in one hand, and a rope in the other, Snagglepuss stepped to the foot of the mountain he was to climb. He surveyed it from top to bottom with an appraising eye.

"Gadzooks, what a challenge!" Snagglepuss exclaimed to himself. "This will take real acting ability!"

For, of course, it was not a real mountain at all, but a make-believe one built in the studio. Nor was it a big mountain. In fact, it was only about twenty feet higher than Snag. So, our great actor had a lot of pretending to do.

"Action!" cried the director.

That was Snagglepuss's cue to start his climb. Slowly and carefully, he placed one foot ahead of the other, using his pick to help in pulling himself upward. For every two forward steps he took, he slipped back one. He fell, then picked himself up again and plodded onward and upward, while the movie cameras rolled and whirred.

"Cut!" cried the director. "You're doing a fine job, Snagglepuss," he added delightedly. "You're really making it look tough."

"I promised you a great performance, sir," our hero replied proudly, "and a Snagglepuss always keeps his word."

"Do it again," the director ordered.

Snagglepuss started at the foot of the mountain once more, putting even greater effort into making it seem that he had been dragging himself up this mountain for days.

Just as he neared the top again, the director stopped him.

"Once more," he ordered. "We need lots more footage on this scene. It's got to look like a long, long climb!"

Again, Snagglepuss pulled his way up the mountain. His feet were getting heavier and heavier with each step. But his eyes were on the peak, which was his goal. He was almost there, at last.

Then the director shouted. "That's far enough. Start from the bottom again."

"Egad," Snagglepuss thought, "I'll never get up in the world at this rate."

By this time, Snagglepuss was no longer acting. As he struggled wearily upward, he was indeed tired, thirsty, and hungry. He felt as if this was the highest mountain in the world, and the summit seemed a long, long way off. Only with desperate effort did he finally reach it. He had succeeded!

"Cut!" cried the director. "That's great!"

Exultantly, Snagglepuss looked down from his place atop the little mountain.

"Granddaddy was right," he mused. "It **is** hard work getting to the top!"

Hanna-Barbera TOUCHÉ and DUM DUM
A TALE OF TWO TURTLES

I WISH WE DIDN'T HAVE TO VISIT YOUR COUSIN TRICKY! HE'S TOO MUCH OF A PRACTICAL JOKER!

WE HAVEN'T BEEN THIS WAY IN A YEAR TO SEE HIM! MAYBE HE'S CHANGED!

HI, COUSIN!

TRICKY! HI!

HA, HA! YOU ALWAYS WERE A GOOD ONE FOR A HAND BUZZER!

HE'S CHANGED ALL RIGHT! HE'S WORSE!

B-Z-Z-Z

THAT WASN'T VERY FUNNY, TRICKY!

HA, HA! I THOUGHT IT WAS!

UH, OH! HERE COMES THE SHERIFF! MAYBE I CAN DITCH HIM AND HAVE SOME FUN AT THE SAME TIME!

40

LEARNING A LESSON

"What are you reading, Yakky?" Chopper asked his little friend.

"A book about judo," Yakky explained. "Someday I may have to protect myself from Fibber Fox when you're not around to help."

"That's right! In fact, you should take lessons. It's much easier to learn when a teacher shows you exactly what to do."

Yakky thought Chopper's idea was a good one, so he set off for town to enroll in a judo class. Someone else thought it was a good idea, too... Fibber Fox! He had been in the bushes hiding and overheard Yakky's plan. He took a shortcut through the woods, stopping at his cave to get a disguise.

A short time later, Yakky was walking down the path to town when he came upon a sign reading, "FREE JUDO LESSONS." An arrow on the sign pointed to a cave, and Yakky flew over and yelled inside that he'd like some lessons. The teacher came out ... it was Fibber Fox with a fake mustache and beard, and Yakky did not recognize him.

"I'd like to take some judo lessons from you," Yakky explained. "I want to be able to protect myself from a nasty old fox."

"It's a good thing you came to me," old Fibber chuckled. "I know exactly how a fox goes about catching a duck. We'll pretend that you're a duck and I'm a fox . . . it shouldn't be too hard. Heh, heh . . . now what would you do if I came at you like this?"

Fibber suddenly leaped for Yakky, shouting, "Aha! After all these years of chasing I've finally got you cornered!"

"You're a good actor," said Yakky, avoiding his teacher. "You act just like a fox! But if you were really that mean Fibber, this is what I would do."

Saying this, Yakky grabbed Fibber by the ankles, upending the nasty old fox with a loud thud. Fibber was rather surprised.

"You really *fell* for that one," Yakky chuckled. "I learned that trick from a judo book I read yesterday."

"That was just luck. I'll get you this time," Fibber growled, rushing toward Yakky again. Yakky didn't move until Fibber went to pounce on him. Then Yakky ducked and poor Fibber went sailing over the little duck's head, right into a stout tree trunk.

"I learned that from the book, too," smiled Yakky, helping his teacher up.

"You read too much," Fibber snarled. "But I'll get you for sure this time."

Fibber slowly stalked toward Yakky, holding his hands out to grab the duck.

"If you were a real fox, I'd get away like *this*," Yakky said as he grabbed Fibber by the wrist and threw him over his shoulder onto the hard ground. "That's in the book."

"I know, I know . . . you learned it from reading," Fibber groaned as he lay on the rocky ground. "I must get *myself* a copy of that book. Lesson is over for today."

"Thank you, sir," Yakky said as he flew off. "It was lots of fun and you're a good teacher. But I'll need more training. I know if I met up with a *real* fox I'd never be able to beat him with my judo holds."

"Bah!" moaned the fractured Fibber. "Yakky still doesn't know I'm the teacher. From now on, I'll stick to gentler sports. This judo is rough on my health. (Groan!)"

The next day Yakky came back for another lesson, but the teacher didn't show up! Yakky couldn't figure out why . . . but we know the answer, don't we? Fibber's a coward!

49

LATER...

BACK, SIMBA! BACK, YOU BEAST!

ARF!

EEEK! HE'S GETTING WILD!

NOW I KNOW WHAT THIS CHAIR IS FOR!

IT'S HOPELESS! IT'S JUST HOPELESS!

(SIGH!) YOU'RE RIGHT! I'LL NEVER HAVE A CIRCUS AND BE A TRAINER! EVEN THAT DOG DIDN'T GIVE ME COURAGE!

OUCH! BUT I THINK HE GAVE ME A FEW FLEAS!

FLEAS... THAT'S IT!

YOU'RE NOT AFRAID OF FLEAS, ARE YOU?

EVEN *I'M* NOT THAT MUCH OF A COWARD!

So...

FRANK FRUMP AND HIS FLEA CIRCUS

UP, BOY! UP!

YOU MIGHT SAY HIS NEW CAREER STARTED FROM *SCRATCH!*

The End

Hanna-Barbera TOP CAT AN ALLEY DOESN'T NECESSARILY MEAN BOWLING

THIS IS AN HEIRLOOM CATNIP BOX! IT BELONGED TO MY GREAT, GREAT GRANDFATHER, FLOP CAT!

(SIGH!) OOPS! IT FINALLY FELL APART!

WHAT'S THAT PIECE OF PAPER, T.C.?

HEY, LOOK AT THIS! IT'S SOME KIND OF OLD DOCUMENT SIGNED BY GOVERNOR GREYLOCKS!

HE WAS THE FIRST MAGISTRATE WHEN THIS WAS JUST A COLONY!

EGAD! ACCORDING TO THIS, THE GOVERNOR GAVE THIS ALLEY TO *FLOP CAT* FOR RIDDING THE CITY OF *MICE!*

GAVE IT TO HIM? LET ME SEE!

"...AND FOR THE TOKEN SUM OF ONE CONTINENTAL COPPER, I TURN THIS PROPERTY OVER TO FLOP CAT!"

(ULP!) I DON'T KNOW WHAT THIS MEANS, BUT I DON'T LIKE IT!

IT MEANS THIS LAND BELONGS TO FLOP CAT'S DESCENDANT, WHO IS TOP CAT!

AND IT MEANS THAT THIS LITTLE STRIP OF LAND IS NOT PART OF THE STATE SINCE IT WAS PRIVATELY OWNED BEFORE THIS *WAS* A STATE! THEREFORE, YOU HAVE NO JURISDICTION HERE, OFFICER!

I'M HAVING THIS DOCUMENT CHECKED!

AFTER A SHORT SEARCH...

GEE, I JUST CAN'T FIGURE IT ...YOU FELLOWS GIVING ME YOUR ALLEY!

HEH, HEH!

WELL, NOW THAT YOU'RE THE OFFICIAL OWNER, WE CAN TELL YOU YOU'RE IN DEBT FOR A BUNDLE OF MONEY ON THE LAND! WE SURE FOOLED YOU!

YOU SURE DID!

YIPE! THE...THE *CITY GOVERNMENT MAN* WAS DIBBLE IN DISGUISE!

I'M TURNING THE ALLEY OVER TO THE CITY AND THEN I'M TURNING YOU CATS OUT OF THE ALLEY!

AND...

HEH, HEH! I GOT ANOTHER COURT ORDER TO EVICT THE CATS! I SHOULD GET A PROMOTION FOR THIS!

CHEER UP, GANG! WE HAVE TO GET OUT OF THAT ALLEY, BUT WE CAN ALWAYS MOVE INTO ANOTHER ONE!

SO...

PROMOTION? I OUGHT TO *FIRE* YOU! THOSE CATS MOVED IN *RIGHT BEHIND US!*

MEOW!

MEOWRR!

POLICE STATION

CHOO CHOO

FANCY FANCY

58

CONGRATS, CAT! WE'VE JUST ELECTED YOU A FULL FLEDGED MEMBER OF THE CLUB!

OH, JOY! REAL FRIENDS AT LAST!

WE ALWAYS HAVE A BIG FEAST WHEN WE GET A NEW MEMBER!

ER... I'D LIKE THAT! BUT I DON'T HAVE A PENNY!

THAT'S OKAY! IT'S *ON US*!

REALLY?

I RAN AWAY FROM HOME TO FIND FRIENDS WHO WOULDN'T JUST LIKE ME FOR MY MONEY... AND I'VE ALREADY FOUND THEM!

Shortly...

THIS IS DELICIOUS! AREN'T YOU EATING?

ER... NO! WE JUST ATE!

JUST YESTERDAY! BUT WE HAVE TO SAVE OUR MONEY TO SPEND ON HIM!

RESTAURANT

FISHBURGERS *our* SPECIALTY

GEE, T.C., I DON'T KNOW IF THIS IS RIGHT!

FAIR IS FAIR! WE BUY HIM A FISHBURGER AND HE BUYS US A SAILBOAT!

NOW LET'S GO TO THE AMUSEMENT PARK AND HAVE SOME FUN!

SWELL!

SHORTLY...

WHEE! I'M GETTING DIZZY!

I'M GETTING DIZZY WATCHING THAT CAT SPEND ALL OUR MONEY!

WE'LL GET IT BACK!

TICKETS

10¢ A RIDE

LATER...

YOU GUYS HAVE BEEN WONDERFUL TO ME AND NOW I HAVE A LITTLE SURPRISE FOR YOU!

REALLY?

I'M NOT REALLY POOR! I'M J. PAUL CATTY, JUNIOR... SON OF A BILLIONAIRE!

I DON'T BELIEVE IT!

AND TO SHOW MY GRATITUDE FOR EVERYTHING, I'M GIVING YOU A BLANK CHEQUE! FILL IN ANY AMOUNT YOU WANT!

A-ANY A-AMOUNT?!

NOW IF YOU'LL EXCUSE ME, I HAVE TO MAKE AN IMPORTANT CALL!

WOW! YOU CAN USE OUR PRIVATE PHONE!

POLICE PHONE

WE CAN BUY THAT SAILBOAT NOW!

SAILBOAT? I CAN BUY A WHOLE NAVY! WE WON'T SETTLE FOR A MEASLY TWO HUNDRED DOLLARS!

WE CAN FILL IN A THOUSAND...TEN THOUSAND!

THAT'S RIGHT, DAD!

62

TOP CAT BENNY THE BALL GOES APE

65

ONE MINUTE LATER, AS BENNY SWINGS FROM TREE TO TREE SHOWING OFF HIS CAPTIVE APE...

I COMMAND YOU BOTH TO STOP IN YOUR TRACKS!

THEY'RE BOTH OUT COLD! NOW I CAN UNDO THE DAMAGE!

THUD!

THUD!

AND SOON...

GEE! WAS I REALLY AS STRONG AS BARZAN?

UH-HUH! BUT WE LIKE YOU BETTER YOUR WEAK OLD WAY!

AND I LIKE THAT APE BETTER BEHIND BARS!

(ULP!) SPEAKING OF BEHIND BARS, HERE COMES DIBBLE! HE'S PROBABLY PLENTY MAD AT US!

DIB, YOU'RE NOT GOING TO ARREST US FOR LETTING THE APE LOOSE AND CAUSING YOU TO FAINT, ARE YOU?

FAINT? I DIDN'T FAINT! I'VE BEEN WORKING SO HARD, I MERELY TOOK A NAP!

ER... BUT YOU DID SEE SOME PECULIAR THINGS!

PECULIAR THINGS? WHY, OF COURSE NOT! I SAW NOTHING AT ALL OUT OF THE ORDINARY!

...AND I'VE GOT TO *KEEP TELLING* MYSELF THAT!

The End

69

And so...

WELL, OFFICER DIBBLE, HOW DO I LOOK?

MUMBLE! MUMBLE!

WITH THIS UNIFORM AND DIBBLE'S LOOKS, I'LL SOON HAVE A FORTUNE IN MY GREEDY HANDS! HEH, HEH!

HEY, BOYS! HERE COMES DIBBLE! NOW REMEMBER! ANYTHING HE SAYS GOES!

FOR A WEEK!

LET'S SEE NOW, THE BACK ENTRANCE TO THE CITY BANK IS DOWN THIS ALLEY!

HIYA, DIBBLE! HOW ARE WE DOIN'?

WHAT?

GOT ANYTHING ELSE YOU'D LIKE US TO DO, DIBBLE?

HUH?

GOOD GRIEF! I CAN'T ROB A BANK WITH SO MANY WITNESSES!

...OR CAN I?

YES, BOYS! I DO HAVE SOMETHING YOU COULD DO FOR ME!

YOU NAME IT!

YES, I CAN USE SOME HELP TRANSFERRING SOME OF THE BANK'S MONEY! IT SEEMS THEY ARE OVERSTOCKED!

CITY BANK EXIT

OKAY, DIBBLE! YOU SHOW US WHERE IT IS... AND WE WILL GET IT!

BUT WHEN HE GETS BACK, HE FINDS THE REAL OFFICER DIBBLE IS FREE OF HIS BONDS...

GOT'CHA! IT'S A GOOD THING YOU NEVER WERE A BOY SCOUT, "BARRY THE BEAK!" IF YOU WERE, YOU'D HAVE LEARNED TO TIE A BETTER KNOT!

OH, FOOEY!

NOW TO RETURN THIS MONEY TO THE BANK AND THEN I'LL BE BACK TO RUN YOU IN TO JAIL!

HEY, TOP CAT, LOOK! DIBBLE IS PUTTING THE MONEY BACK IN THE BANK!

HE'S WHAT?

CITY BANK
EXIT

HEY! WHERE DID YOU GET THAT?

YOU DROPPED IT ...REMEMBER?

WELL, THANKS! NOW, GET LOST AGAIN!

SWISH!

I'VE CHANGED MY MIND AGAIN, FELLAS...DIBBLE IS SO TWO-FACED I WOULDN'T BE SURPRISED TO SEE HIM RUNNING HIMSELF IN SOME DAY!

DON'T LOOK NOW, T.C., BUT...

...THAT'S EXACTLY WHAT HE'S DOING NOW!

GET GOIN'!

The End

Touché and Dum Dum
Hanna-Barbera
HOW TO BECOME A NEW TURTLE

I JUST FEEL KIND OF TIRED AND WORN OUT! I DON'T EVEN FEEL LIKE HOLLERING, *TOUCHE AND AWAY!*

YOU ALWAYS TAKE CARE OF EVERYBODY ELSE! NOW I'M TAKING CARE OF YOU BY TAKING YOU TO THE DOCTOR!

AT THE DOCTOR'S OFFICE...

YOU'RE JUST ONE TERRIBLY TIRED-TYPE TURTLE! YOU'VE BEEN DOING TOO MANY GOOD DEEDS!

THUMP!

WHAT YOU NEED IS A DAY OF UTTER AND COMPLETE RELAXATION!

WHERE CAN I GO FOR THAT, DOC?

THERE'S THE PERFECT PLACE! SPEND A DAY AT THE CIRCUS! IT'LL MAKE YOU FEEL LIKE A NEW MAN... ER, TURTLE!

AJAX CIRCUS

79

CLOSE FRIENDS

"Boo hoo!" sobbed little Yakky Doodle. "My pond has all dried up and turned to mud!"

"Aw, now, don't you cry, little feller," soothed his friend, Chopper, who came along just then. "We'll find you another pond or a pool of water."

"We will?" asked Yakky, brightening.

"Why, sure," said Chopper confidently. "There's a pool right over that way . . . no, it's over the other way . . . no . . . well, there must be one around here, somewhere," he finished. "Come on, we'll go look."

"You're sure a real good friend, Chopper," beamed Yakky, as they started off.

"And you're a real good friend, too," Chopper smiled at the little duckling.

"Does that mean we are close friends, Chopper?" Yakky asked. "I've always wanted a close friend."

"We're close friends," replied Chopper.

Before long, they heard water splashing and turned toward the sound. Then, "It's a fancy garden fountain," said Chopper.

"But it's water!" exclaimed Yakky, hopping into the lower section of the fountain. Then, "Ooh," he gasped, as the water rushed over him. "That's not for me!"

Before long, they came to a birdbath.

"Oh, boy!" exclaimed little Yakky, heading for the bath. "That's a dandy pool."

Yakky jumped into the birdbath and swam around happily. "This is great," he said. "I think I'll stay a while."

"That's good," said Chopper, turning away, relieved that Yakky's problem was solved for a time. A moment later, however, Yakky shouted, "Help, Chopper!"

Running back, Chopper found three big blackbirds zooming down at little Yakky!

"This is **our** bath!" the birds screeched.

"Get out of it, you duck! Get out! O-U-T!"

Chopper quickly scooped up his little friend to safety. "All right, all right," he growled at the birds, "he's leaving."

Yakky and Chopper walked on and on, but they found no pond or pool of water. At last, discouraged and weary, Chopper said, "Let's go home and rest awhile."

"All right, Chopper," Yakky agreed. Then he sighed, "I don't think I'll ever find another pool of water, for my own."

"Oh, sure you will," Chopper said, with an assurance he did not feel.

As they neared Chopper's doghouse, Yakky exclaimed, "You're right, Chopper! **There's** a little pool I can have for my own . . . your pan full of drinking water!" As Yakky splashed in the water, he said, "Now we'll really be close friends, Chopper! We'll always be together! Isn't that nice?"

"Oh, yeah, sure," Chopper agreed. But he groaned to himself, "Oh, no! He's a nice little feller, but that's too close! I won't get any rest with him around!"

Chopper lay down to ponder his problem, while Yakky frolicked in the water. Meanwhile, the sky grew dark and cloudy.

Then, "It's raining! It's raining!" cried Yakky in delight. "My pond will get full of water again, and I can go back to it!" Looking at Chopper, he apologized, "I'm sorry to leave you, Chopper, but a pond is really the best place for a little duck, like me. You understand, don't you?"

"Sure, I understand," Chopper grinned.

"And we'll still be close friends?" Yakky asked.

"We'll still be close friends," Chopper assured him, adding under his breath, "but not too close, thank goodness."

Printed and bound in England by Jarrold & Sons Ltd, Norwich